A spiritual conversation at Starbucks between three high school friends

Greg Stier

D2S Publishing

D2S Publishing

Venti Jesus Please
Copyright © 2008, 2010 by Dare 2 Share Ministries, Inc.
Revised and updated.
All rights reserved.

A D2S Publishing book
PO Box 745323
Arvada, CO 80006

Editor: Jane Dratz

Stier, Greg.
Venti Jesus Please: A spiritual conversation at Starbucks
between three high school friends
ISBN-13: 978-0-9725507-7-2

Library of Congress Control Number: 2009944004
Printed in the United States of America

1

Our Friday night lay before us extending the sweet promise of freedom. Spring was in the air, which was perfect, since it was opening night for Brentwood High's spring musical. We three were totally stoked about the show because one of our best friends was playing the lead. But we had a couple hours to kill before curtain time. Time for some liquid refreshment.

Piling into my brand new, bright red Scion—a birthday present from the old man—we headed off to one of our favorite hangouts. Starbucks. The music

VENTI JESUS PLEASE

blared as we traveled our well-worn path toward the ice-cold Frappuccinos.

It was going to be a long night—the caffeine infusion would help us go the distance. Besides the play itself, the after-party would probably go until early morning. And what usually happened after the after-party was a hangover.

But we'd earned it. As seniors at Brentwood we were riding high and just a few months away from ultimate freedom—a.k.a. graduation. Four years at one of the most academically rigorous high schools in the city and we'd all made it, mostly with flying colors. So we deserved the pressure release valve tonight's party would provide. Maybe this time I could even talk Nick into joining us.

Little did I know that the next hour or so at Starbucks would hijack my plans.

That night's highly anticipated performance of *Grease* was a big deal to us. While none of us three were in the musical, Kailey was—the missing member of our tight little clique. She was playing the lead female role and we couldn't wait to cheer her on from the front row.

The "Look at me, I'm Sandra D" jokes had been flowing ever since she'd landed the part of Sandy after winter break. Kailey took it all with a great big smile. She'd been in past plays and musicals, but this was her final shot at glory at Brentwood. We all knew that down deep inside she was hoping this role would be the beginning of something bigger— much bigger.

Before I get much further into my story, let me introduce myself. I'm Jared. Let's see, how would I describe myself? I don't want to brag…okay, I'll brag just a little. I'm a good-looking jock, tall, quasi-ripped (100 push-ups a day) and fairly popular. Let's just say I've never had a problem getting the girls to hang with me.

Track is my sport of choice. I run pretty freakin' fast. In fact, a few months ago I snagged an athletic scholarship to San Diego State, full ride. Dad tried to act happy, but I think he was disappointed I didn't get a full ride at USC like my big bother, I mean, brother, Jake. After all, USC is a private school, while San

VENTI JESUS PLEASE

Diego's just a lowly public university—no prestige in that. Dad didn't say anything, but he wears his disappointment like his cologne…thick.

My dad can crush you with a raised eyebrow. I know from personal experience. His disapproving glances have smashed my ego many times.

Never good enough. Never fast enough. Never smart enough.

Even my 3.7 GPA isn't good enough for him. Jake made the 4.0 "hall of fame" in our house, so by falling short of perfection by .3, I've failed to measure up. But enough about me. I'm starting to depress myself.

Instead, let me tell you a little about my friends who were with me on that late afternoon jaunt to Starbucks.

Jen is one of the school's "pretty girls." But unlike most of them, she isn't stuck-up. She's down to earth and real. Her long blond hair and flashing blue eyes can lead you to believe that she's just a pretty face, but there's more to her than meets the eye.

Jen loves to have fun. To be honest, she has a little bit of a bad girl in her. I've noticed over the past year that she's been looking for love in all the wrong places. She's a hottie who knows all the right people and goes to all the right parties. She's gotten in trouble a few times for some of the things she's inhal...I mean tried. But, for the most part, Jen is working harder than usual, trying to get her act together for graduation.

Jen's family situation is radically different from mine. Her mom is a devout Catholic and her dad is a devoted alcoholic. She has chosen a party "purgatory" in between. But, in her words, she leans more toward daddy's hell than mom's heaven. Jen told me once that she's just out for all the fun she can get—just like you're supposed to be at this age. But sometimes she just seems really confused about life.

Me? Inwardly, I like Jen's rebellious streak. And lately I've been attracted to more than just her attitude toward life. We've been good friends a long time, but as I've watched her get hurt by guy after guy during junior and senior year, the chemistry between us has started shifting some recently. I'm a little nervous about us moving down this new road, but hey, maybe it's time to stop fighting the feelings if we're both interested and things are percolating under the surface anyway.

Jen's the one who's pulled me into the partying scene, though I'm more careful than she is, because, well, I'm a jock and don't want to tick off my ultra-conservative track coach. Caution is warranted on that front. After all, logic and ambition are the twin pillars of how I was taught to live, so I'm not much concerned about any "moral" issues. I've got no religious background at all, actually. Besides, Dad is always overbooked on the weekends, so even if we did believe in God we probably would never go to church. Dad is too busy worshipping at the altar of the Almighty Dollar.

I guess if you were to put a religious label on me, it would be "atheist." I really don't believe in God. To be honest, I don't know how a God that is good could allow so much suffering in the world.

CHAPTER 1

I was in Mexico last year on a rare family vacation. Somehow we got lost in the barrio and I witnessed poverty like I couldn't believe. Little kids covered in grime, living in tin and cardboard shanties—everyone using the same dirty stream of garbage-filled water. I guess it shook me up some.

At that moment, I decided deep down that if there was a God, he was cruel, or at the very minimum, distant and uncaring. I didn't want to have anything to do with him. The way I saw it, if he wasn't going to be there for me someday if I was really in need, then why would I want to be there for him?

But that presents a problem. Why? Because my long-time track buddy and best friend on the planet is a blatant Christian. He is the final person in our foursome, and, in many ways, the heart and soul of our quirky little "Four Musketeers" clique.

Now 99% of the Christians I've met over the years at school seem to fall into one of two categories: they're either whacked-out or hypocrites. The nut jobs stick out like a flashing neon sign. These are the kids who wear Christ on their sleeves (some literally). They generally act like they have all the answers and take on the science teachers with talk of Adam and Eve and stories about "intelligent design" (whatever that is…I wouldn't call whoever "designed" the mosquito all that intelligent). But I digress… Anyway, these Jesus-loving dorks stand around flagpoles, demand their rights, and walk the halls in their weird, cheesy t-shirts.

I remember one guy in particular who always invited me to go to youth group with him. He had the persistence of a bulldog and, to be honest, was totally annoying. He would always be telling me that it was bowling night or pizza night or game night. To be honest, it all sounded way too Amish to me.

I know the real reason he wanted me to show up was to give me a Jesus sales pitch and convert me from my "heathen ways." Not interested. I'll never understand Christians who try to trick you into saying some words and becoming part of "the fold." Feels manipulative to me.

The other kind of Christian is annoying for a whole different reason. Hypocrites are easy to spot. They claim the label of Jesus, but don't much follow what he said. When they're with their little Christian friends, they look and talk and act all Christian. But I've seen many of them at the same parties I go to. They're usually the first to grab a drink and the last to stagger out. Ironically, more wasted than me...

That leaves the 1%.

That leaves Nick.

It's kind of hard to describe Nick. Starting freshman year, we were on the track team together—same relay team—so our friendship was born out of sweat and shared dreams. He's not part of the "in crowd" of Southern California cool. His brown hair looks like a sheepdog, and his build is more lanky than ripped, but there's something genuine about him that I like—and that I respect.

Maybe it's because when he asks you "how ya doing?" he really wants to know. He seems to treat everyone like he really cares. Or maybe it's because I've never seen him compromise his values, not once—believe me, I've tried to get him to! Maybe it's because I know that he's really sold out to his beliefs. I don't buy it or really understand it, but I know he does...hook, line and sinker. His sincerity draws me in. He's not fake. This is why I like hanging with Nick.

Now don't get me wrong, he and I have pulled our share of pranks. But I haven't seen him cross the line into malicious. There was one time, though, where he got really mad at me for something I said. I'll never forget him coming to me the next day and asking my forgiveness. I've never had anyone genuinely ask me for forgiveness for anything. Even though we go way back, it kinda left me stunned. I wish my dad and I could have just one moment like that. But the pride is so thick in our house that if it were smoke, we'd all suffocate.

I guess converting the heathen is part of being Christian—because Nick has tried to talk to me about God several times. I know some Bible stories and they totally sound like a bunch of fairy tales to me. So I've just shut Nick down every time he's tried to bring it up. I've always just told him "No offense, but I'm not into the whole religion thing." He'd always come back with, "But I'm not talking about religion, I'm talking about Jesus!"

My response? To shut him down, and then I'd just clam up until he shut up…and he always did.

So there we were, three unlikely friends pushing open the door to our favorite Starbucks, killing some time before the show. The air was electric. Spring was upon us and one of our best friends was about to star in *Grease*.

2

The familiar Starbucks smells and sounds greeted us as we lined up—our home away from home. We ordered and friendly banter took over as we waited for the hot female barista to make our cold drinks.

"I'm kinda thinkin' I'm becoming a caffeine addict," Nick commented as he grabbed his Frappe from the counter.

"Yeah, Christian crack!" Jen shot back.

We all laughed. Jen is quick with the comebacks and is continually, but good-naturedly, making fun of Nick and his straight-up lifestyle.

VENTI JESUS PLEASE

After the rest of us retrieved our caffeinated concoctions, we staked our claim on the big comfortable chairs in the corner—the quietest part of this particular Starbucks, where the half wall separated us from the loud "WHIRRING" sound of the mega espresso machine.

For a few minutes our conversation was focused on Kailey and *Grease*. We all took pride in Kailey's stardom. Each of us had taken our turn at listening to her vent about all the drama queens she'd put up with in rehearsals these past months. But we'd supported and encouraged her along the way, just like we Four Musketeers always did for each other. All for one, and one for all. Tonight, we'd all be basking in her bright lights and applause lines.

But a few sips into our conversation, the pleasant small talk took an unexpected turn into a risky subject. And much to my surprise, I was at the steering wheel.

It was the headline of the coffee-stained *New York Times* on the little table next to our cushy chairs that caught my attention. I reached over while Jen

CHAPTER 2

and Nick were joking around about something
and read the six bold words across the top of the
newspaper.

Top Evangelical Pastor Caught in Adultery

After skimming the first paragraph of the front
page spread, I couldn't contain my repulsion and let
loose my own six startling words. "All Christians are
just plain hypocrites!" I announced shaking my head
in disgust.

As I spewed out these words with more venom
than I had originally intended, both Jen and Nick
abruptly ceased their conversation and looked at
me curiously. I flung the paper across the coffee
table toward Nick, just to get a rise out of him. Like a
Vegas Blackjack dealer's card throw, the paper slid
across the table and landed right in front of him.

He picked up the article and started reading
it. As he did, he began subconsciously shaking his
head. The pained look on his face intensified the
further he read.

VENTI JESUS PLEASE

"Whoa. Whoa. Whoa, just kidding, Nick," I joked. "Don't cry or anything, dude. I was just messing with you."

But Nick stayed silent, ignoring my jab. The vein in his neck was pulsing and I started to wonder if he might burst a blood vessel. Calm, patient Nick. This was weird.

"What's wrong?" Jen asked, trying to draw him out.

"This makes me sick!" Nick exploded, totally out of character. "This guy is supposed to be a pastor, and he's out doing stuff like this. What was he thinking? How stupid is he?"

"Calm down, man," I ventured.

"You don't get it, Jared." Nick was seething. "I know what it's like to have your parents screw up and totally mess your life up, right along with their own. Look at this picture of him with his wife and kids with the media swarming around. Look at this guy's kids. They look totally shell-shocked."

Nick barely came up for a breath before he continued venting. "Remember, my mom's been through three husbands and counting—this is personal. Every time my mom heads into one of her 'romantic relationships,' I cringe and brace myself for what I know is coming in the end—disaster. It's gotta be ten times worse to go through it all in full view of the media, and the whole world, for that matter."

Then suddenly, it was the weirdest thing, but the anger seemed to just drain out of him like somebody had pulled the plug and his voice softened. "Didn't he think about how much cheating on his wife would hurt his family, his church, the reputation of God himself…?

"Wait a minute," Nick continued quietly. "What am I doing here, who am I to pass judgment on him…that's God's job, not mine. After all, I'm a hypocrite too, just like him," he said with absolute seriousness.

Friends for such a long time and I still get surprised by Nick. Of all the words I expected out of his mouth, I didn't think he'd be lumping himself in with this preacher. To be honest, I really just wanted to diffuse this religion talk and move on. The last thing I wanted was to leave the door open for a long-winded response. We'd been having a great time. Before I could say anything, Jen beat me to the punch.

"You're not a hypocrite, Nick. Come on, dude, if every Christian were like you, then maybe I'd become one, too."

"I am a hypocrite, Jen. I haven't gone out and done the adultery thing like this guy, but I know that I consistently screw up what God wants for my life. Look at me just now…it's obvious I'm not a very forgiving person. You can tell I'm still angry at my mom and the mess she's made of her life. And that's just the beginning. I can't possibly live up to the message of Jesus consistently. I've lied. I've lusted. I'm obviously still bitter. I fall short everyday."

Trying to lighten the mood, I joked, "You've lusted? Have you ever lusted after Jen? Or is it me that you want?"

Have you ever told a joke that fell like a steaming turd on the sidewalk? Well, that was what happened. Jen and Nick ignored me like the turd never fell.

And then it just got quiet. Painfully quiet.

The awkward silence was palpable as we all just sat there, no one talking, everyone sipping. Nick continued reading the newspaper article. Jen, who doesn't like conflict, was kind of staring off into space. Afraid of saying something stupid again, I chose to just keep my mouth shut.

Nick finally broke the silence, "For me, Christianity isn't a club or a philosophy or a religious ideal that I have to live up to. No, it's all about a relationship with Jesus—a relationship that's continually changing me from the inside out and drawing me deeper and closer to God. It's a growing process. But the process is never fully or finally complete and because of that, in some ways, Christians always fall short of what Jesus intended. It's in that sense that every Christian, including me, is a hypocrite."

My brain was racing in a bunch of directions and all at the same time. Here was one of the most considerate guys on the planet, in my experience, telling me he was a hypocrite. Sometimes Christians just didn't make sense. First, they try to live up to a standard that they agree no one can keep. They all talk about "believing in Jesus," but then in the next breath say you have to have some kind of "relationship" with a guy who's been dead for a couple of thousand years. But I couldn't remember anyone, anywhere, saying that being a hypocrite was OK with God…if you believe in God.

Jen's reply pulled me out of my head and back into the conversation. "I think you're being way too tough on yourself, Nick. Sometimes people do things that are unforgivable. When my dad's on one of his binges, he says stuff that's burned into my memory forever. Things I can't forgive or forget. If you ask me, none of us needs to forgive our parents for the hell they've put us through. They don't deserve it."

"You don't understand, Jen," Nick countered. "It's different for me, because I'm claiming to be a Jesus-follower. You see, forgiveness is at the center of Jesus' teachings and what he came to earth to do. Sometimes I'm still not very good at forgiveness. But like I said, it's a process, it takes time…"

"That kind of makes sense," she said, obviously mulling this novel idea. "If Jesus 'saves' you, or whatever, from your sins, I guess it takes a little time...but when the pain is really screaming, I just can't forgive and make it all go away." After a brief pause she added, "Sounds kind of hopeless to me." Whenever Jen sounded this tone, it tugged at my heart in an uncomfortable way.

But Nick jumped back in by saying, "It's not hopeless at all because—"

I cut him off. I knew he was about to launch into his whole religion versus relationship talk, so I decided to throw him a curve ball. "Okay, since we're being honest here, let me ask you an honest question, Nick."

"Go ahead," he replied.

Scooting forward on my chair, I looked straight in his eyes and asked, "If Christianity is for hypocrites, why did you get so shook up when you looked at that newspaper article? I mean, it shouldn't have surprised you, right?" Expecting that I'd landed a direct hit, I sat back and waited for his response.

3

"Because I get sick of it," Nick answered bluntly.

"Sick of what?" Jen asked.

"Sick of the message Christians are sending to the world! Yes, we all fall short of what Jesus intended, but guys like this don't even seem to be trying to serve Jesus, and it makes me mad!

"This preacher was known in the media for railing against homosexual sin," Nick went on. "He organized petitions to get civil unions among homosexuals outlawed and all that jazz. The article says that he was the largest single voice in getting gay marriage banned in several states all across America. Meanwhile, he's been cheating on his wife. Too many times we're sending the message that Christianity is about pointing fingers at everyone else who isn't keeping our list of rules and regulations. Meanwhile, we're ignoring the rules ourselves."

"Wait a minute," Jen interrupted, "isn't the Christian religion all about 'the rules'? I mean isn't that what all religions are? My mom is a full-on Catholic. I don't know all that much about what she believes, 'cause it's kinda a forbidden topic around our house. When I was really little, I raised a fuss once about having to go to church with her, and my dad told me I didn't need to go ever again, and I haven't gone back since I was like six years old.

"Lots of fights about that between my parents," Jen continued, rolling her eyes. "But the way I understand it, my mom *has* to go to confession, to Mass, pray to Mary, say the Rosary, and who knows what else. She's got all sorts of rules and regulations that she thinks she has to keep in order to pass the big test and be good enough to go to heaven someday."

Nick countered, "Jen, God doesn't care if you're Catholic or Baptist or whatever. It doesn't matter which church you go to. God doesn't look at the team we're on. But everyone trusts in something during their life. He judges us based on what we're trusting our lives to, whether it's ourselves, rules, good deeds, or him. It's what a person does with Jesus that matters."

I knew it was coming. The relationship speech Nick had been trying to give me for years was on. Jen seemed to actually be interested in this stuff, so this time it looked like there was nothing I could do about it.

What I did know about religion and rules didn't seem to fit with where Nick was heading, though. I knew enough to realize that rules don't go very far in making for a good relationship. If any of my girlfriends ever made a rule that I had to love them, how lame would that be? A cold, one-sided relationship. I'd be like a robot.

Jen interrupted my thoughts by asking, "What do you mean by 'it's what a person does with Jesus that matters'? And what could Jesus possibly have to do with the decisions I make in my life?"

Nick thought for awhile and began, "Well, there are two types of people who call themselves 'Christians' out there. One is the 'rules Christian' who sees Jesus as a good example that we must live up to, and then maybe, just maybe, we'll meet him someday in heaven...if we're good enough, that is."

"And the other type?" I asked.

"The other type is the type that knows that there is no possible way we could ever live up to the example of Jesus, so we give up trying…"

"Whoa! Wait a minute!" I interrupted, "I'm an atheist and even I don't think a person should give up trying to be like Jesus. Besides, isn't this a part of being in the 'Christian club'?"

"Let me explain, Jared. I wasn't finished. This other type of Christian—and I count myself among them—knows that following all the rules is impossible.

Instead, they give up trying to be like Jesus and start trusting him with their life."

"I don't understand," Jen said, shaking her head slowly.

"*We* don't understand," I emphasized.

"Okay, let me back up a little bit so we can get the big picture, okay?" Nick offered.

I cringed inside at this comment. Sounded like the makings for a long, boring version of *Jesus for Dummies*, but since this was Nick—my best bud—I stifled the sarcasm and instead said, "Okay, you've been trying to tell me about Jesus for years, right?"

"Yeah, but every time I try, you shut me down, bro!"

"Well, you're on stage now. Better go for it while you have the chance," I said while glancing over at Jen's nodding head and riveted eyes. I swallowed hard. "I'll probably have a few questions along the way that I may drill you with, if that's okay."

VENTI JESUS PLEASE

"Sure!" Nick said. "Bring it, atheist!"

We all laughed, but the look of intensity in Nick's eyes stirred up my concern for Jen, knowing she was a more vulnerable target for some of this stuff. I knew I didn't have all the answers. But I was confident that I was not going to let him push me or Jen into some twisted logic corner and convert us. It was best to let him know that up front.

"Just don't get your feelings hurt and fall apart when I grill you," I warned.

"Jared!" Jen scolded, throwing a stir stick at me.

"I'm kidding! I'm kidding!" I blurted, while trying to catch the tiny projectile. But I really wasn't.

"Before I share this story with you, I want to make one thing perfectly clear," Nick announced assertively.

"What's that?" asked Jen.

CHAPTER 3

"I'm not going to try to force either of you to buy into Christianity, real Christianity, that is. I'm just going to paint a picture that you can choose to either accept or reject."

I responded right away. "Fair enough. And I won't try to convert you to atheism, I'll just paint a picture of atheism for you that you can choose to accept or reject."

"Agreed," Jen and Nick said almost simultaneously.

"Well, the story starts in a garden," Nick began.

"Wait! No 'once upon a time' or anything?" Jen teased.

"No. Because it's not a fairy tale, Jen," Nick responded with a slight smile.

"Let me guess, the Garden of Eden, right?" I said, trying to get the conversation back on track, figuring the quicker we got through this, the better.

VENTI JESUS PLEASE

"Right!" Nick answered. "In the beginning God created—"

"So you're one of those creationism freaks are you, Nick? Come on, bro, I thought you were brighter than that!" I could tell my words stung a bit, but I had my limits.

Before Nick could respond, Jen interrupted, "Wait a minute, what do you mean, creationism freak?"

I jumped in before Nick could. "Creationism is the belief that God created everything in the universe, including the first man and woman, Adam and Eve. Creationists believe that God put them in a beautiful place called the Garden of Eden where they lived in peace and harmony, walking around naked eating apples. Isn't that right, Nick?"

I could tell Nick was surprised I knew this much when he asked, "Where did you learn that? Did you go to Sunday school when you were little?"

"Nah!" I answered. "The only time I've ever been on the inside of a church was for my cousin's wedding. I learned it from the Christian nerds in my science classes the last couple years! I've heard all their little arguments. They're idiots!"

"You can count me in as one of those idiots, Jared," Nick responded calmly, but his words brought me up short.

Jen's eyes turned toward me and I knew I was in a good spot, so I started to defend my position by attacking his. "Come on, Nick. You don't really buy into all that stuff about Adam and Eve in an environmentally friendly garden of bliss, do you?"

Nick was quiet for a moment and then out of nowhere he said, "I've got to use the restroom." With that he quickly grabbed his backpack and walked away.

4

Jen and I just kind of sat there, surprised at how abruptly Nick had left.

"That was weird," Jen whispered.

"Well, when you gotta pee, you gotta pee," I replied, not bothering to lower my voice.

Pointing to his empty Venti, I said, "The boy's got a Grande bladder, but is living in a Venti world."

Jen laughed so hard she snorted. The guys I'd noticed checking her out earlier were checking her out again, but this time for a different reason.

VENTI JESUS PLEASE

While she was pulling herself together, I started thinking again about Nick. Nick—a creationist nerd?! This was embarrassing. Believing in God was one thing, but this Adam and Eve stuff was another. What was he thinking? Anyway, Jen would back me up. Besides, first question and he was already running scared.

After a few minutes, Nick came back and asked if we could all move to a table. We agreed. As we grabbed our drinks, I started giving him a hard time for taking his backpack into the restroom with him. "Don't you trust us, dude? Think I'm going to steal your Bible or something?"

He just laughed. It was kind of weird when Nick just stood there and waited for us to be seated first at one of the bigger tables. He then took the seat directly across from Jen and me. But before I could think more about it, he jumped back in.

"Okay, first off, there are lots of beliefs within Christianity. I know it may seem to you like Christianity is just one set of beliefs, but Christians have a lot of different views about Creationism and Intelligent Design and a bunch of other theories about how everything in the universe began. Some Christians think that God created the entire universe out of nothing by literally speaking it into existence in a short amount of time. And some Christians believe God used evolution to create life as we know it, including the very first people."

"What do you believe?" I asked.

"I believe that God created everything out of nothing," Nick replied. "And we can talk more about how I came to my conclusions another time. But the most important part to remember is that most all Christians believe that the earth and all the life on it didn't just happen randomly, it was part of God's plan. And people and their freedom to make choices are part of God's plan, too."

I sat there shaking my head and finally said, "But Nick, scientists have pretty much proven that God doesn't exist."

Suddenly Nick's head went down. His hands were under the table and he just stared downward like he was deep in thought. Jen and I looked at each other. There must have been like sixty seconds of very awkward silence at the table. I thought maybe it was a Christian thing. Maybe he was shook up and praying or something. After all, I was drilling him with some pretty tough questions.

"No, they haven't," Nick finally said as his head came back up. "In fact, at both the micro and macro level, many scientists are concluding that an Intelligent Designer may be the best explanation for life as we know it. On the micro level, the incredible complexity of our DNA shouts that there was a designer behind it. Bill Gates, the Microsoft billionaire dude, has compared human DNA to a computer program, except he acknowledges that DNA is far, far more advanced than anything computer programmers have ever come up with. Just think of that, how complicated and beyond most of us computers are, and yet the human body's DNA is somehow programmed to be way, way more intricate and complex. How could that all just happen by chance?"

Nick's head dropped down again and he was silent for several seconds. Maybe it was the way he centered himself, kind of like the lotus meditation position for Christians or something.

CHAPTER 4

"And on the macro level, looking at the whole cosmos," he said, jumping back in, "evolutionary scientists who believe in the Big Bang theory accept the reality that there had to be a distinct beginning to the universe, a point where matter first appeared. Science can't explain where that very first matter came from. But everything comes from something, so there must have been a 'first cause' that triggered that very first beginning point of matter's existence. Many scientists believe the most logical explanation for that something is a supernatural being, an Intelligent Designer."

"I don't buy it," I said skeptically.

"Okay, well then, think about it this way," Nick said, glancing over at Jen who gave him one of her kind-hearted, encouraging smiles. "I believe that God created everything, right?"

"If you say so," I agreed.

"And you believe there was no supernatural being involved in the development of life as we know it, that everything in the evolutionary process has happened by chance," Nick continued. "Right?"

"Yes," I stated bluntly.

"But neither of us can reproduce this in the lab. So, both you and I are exercising faith by believing what we believe."

"Blind faith?" I asked with just a hint of sarcasm.

"Not blind faith," Nick answered. "I think God provides enough evidence so that I'm not taking a blind leap of faith. As a matter of fact, I think it's a leap into the light and not a leap into the darkness.

"When you think about it, both you and I have faith in something. You trust that blind fate over millions of years made our universe, every animal, bug and human through evolution. I trust that the Bible is true and that God created everything in the universe. All of us have to have some level of faith to believe what we believe. Right?"

"Yeah, I guess so," I acknowledged, "though I've never seen myself as having faith in anything." When I noticed a hurt look flash across Jen's face, I added quickly, "Except my best friends, of course.

But Nick, now that you put it that way, I guess I have put my faith in science."

Nick pulled his chair closer to the table and continued, "So if each of us exercises faith, my question to you is, which takes more faith to believe? That an infinite God created everything that exists, or that the incredible complexities and fine-tuning of everything—from our human bodies to the laws of physics governing the cosmos—happened by mere chance?"

Neither Jen nor I had a quick answer, so Nick forged ahead. "Let me explain it a different way. Let's say I took your iPhone apart and separated it out into a hundred pieces. Let's say I took all those pieces and put them in a paper sack. I shake the bag up, dig a hole and bury it. Let's say I come back in fifty years and dig the bag up. What are the chances of your phone being put back together all by itself."

"Zero to none," was Jen's reply.

"Jared?" asked Nick.

VENTI JESUS PLEASE

"I'll tell you something right now," I joked, "if you took my iPhone apart, put it in a bag and buried it, then I'd take you apart and bury you, dude. It's worth more than my life!"

"Okay, okay," Jen said, throwing me a dismissive look. "Nick, what's your point about his phone in pieces in the paper bag?"

"All I'm saying is this," Nick replied, "the universe is much more complicated than an iPhone. DNA, physics, chemistry, planetary orbits, how a body works and a whole bunch of other things are all way more complicated and precisely fine-tuned for life than the theory of evolution can explain. So I believe that God had to be right smack in the middle of the creative process. And like I said before, I'm not the only one. More and more scientists are accepting the idea of God as a reasonable explanation for the creation of this complex universe. Because something had to have created the very first stuff that all of life came from—there had to be some sort of first cause that caused the rest."

"Good point. I've gotta go pee," I replied. I got up, and headed off, looking for relief.

5

I wasn't sure what to think about this conversation, but it was starting to make me a little uncomfortable. Billions of years, probability and God are all impossible to get your   mind around. I agree that no one can know for sure how everything got started. So Nick was right about that, everyone has faith in something.

Maybe there really was some supernatural force that had a hand in creating life. Could there actually be a God? And a bunch of rules we were supposed to follow so God would like us? What if there really was some great judge in the sky who was the extreme version of my dad—always watching me, always judging me, distant and disappointed? The thought was both intriguing and depressing at the same time in an odd sort of way.

When I returned, I found Nick and Jen deep in conversation, so I just sat down and listened in for a few minutes. Jen was saying, "I guess I don't understand why all this talk of how everything began matters so much. I thought you were going to tell us the story of Christianity. What does it matter whether we were created or we evolved by random chance?"

"The first 4 words in the Bible are 'in the beginning God,'" Nick offered. "The rest of the whole Bible and Jesus' part of the story won't make any sense unless you start with those 4 words. It matters, too, because it determines how you view yourself. If you evolved through random natural selection, then, in one way, you are the result of a pretty cold process. You are who you are. You were born. You live. You're going to die. And then that's it. You're worm food after that. And while you live, it doesn't really matter what you do with your life. After all it's 'survival of the fittest,' right?"

"Yeah, I guess," Jen conceded.

"But believing in God makes it a whole different story," Nick went on. "If God made you in his image and for his glory, then you have purpose in your life. You were created by him to be in relationship with him to bring him glory."

Jen interrupted, "What do you mean by that word 'glory'?"

"Sorry, Jen, sometimes Christian words make things impossible to understand. Here's what I'm actually trying to say—if God created you, then you have a higher purpose than just living out your eighty-some years and dying, and that is to acknowledge him, serve him and worship him. You have a bigger purpose and deeper meaning for your life—that's the relationship part. In this life we relate to him, and when we die we can spend forever with him in heaven."

"Does that higher purpose stuff mean that if I was a Christian I would actually know what I wanted to do with my life after I graduate? Like whether I should go to college or not, or what to major in, or where to get a job?" Jen asked with a playful tone.

Nick started in with an answer, but my mind wandered off as I thought about Jen's situation. Despite her teasing tone, I sensed there was an underlying edge to her question. She'd been wrestling lately with the big question of what to do after high school. It'd been weighing on her pretty heavy since January, when all the college apps had been due. She was dying to get out of the house and away from her parents, but she really wasn't sure she wanted to do the college thing right away, since she didn't know what she wanted to study anyway. And money was tight around her house this past year, ever since her dad had lost his job.

Nick's voice drew my mind back to the present. "...so being a Christian doesn't give you a crystal ball to gaze into as you map out your future plans. But it does give you a solid, underlying sense of what God wants you to be about as you live the life he's given you. It's really all about being in a day-by-day—er, actually, a moment-by-moment—relationship with him and telling others about how they can know him and be transformed by his love and forgiveness too."

This direction in the conversation was getting too real for me. I'd way rather talk about some long ago mythical characters, so when I sensed a pause in the conversation, I interrupted, "Hey guys, while I was sitting on the can, I thought of another question."

"Ewww. Thanks for the mental picture, Jared!" Jen wrinkled up her nose and hit me in the arm hard.

"Shoot," said Nick.

"The whole Adam, Eve, apple thing about breaking God's rules—do you really believe all that?" I asked.

"Okay, okay, sorry, I'm having to play Bible catch up again here, guys," Jen interrupted. "All this religion stuff is basically a forbidden topic at my house—way too full of landmines to ever talk about in my family. So will someone please tell me where an apple ties into the story of Christianity?"

VENTI JESUS PLEASE

I looked over at Nick and said, "Let me try and bring her up to speed. Okay?"

"Sure," he said, nodding. "You've been trained by the Bible nerd squad in biology class, right? Go for it, but I'll spot you."

So I launched in, saying, "Okay, so the story goes that God creates Adam and Eve and they're living together in the garden in perfect harmony. Did I mention that they were naked?"

"Yes," answered Jen, "twice now. Why are you so fixated on the word 'naked'?"

I informed her that all guys liked to walk around the house naked and they loved to see naked girls. "God made us guys that way. Right, Nick?"

"I guess so…but I didn't know about the naked house walking stuff," Nick replied. "Maybe that's just an atheist thing, Jared," he added sarcastically.

I continued, unhindered by the friendly shot, "Anyway, the story goes that Adam and Eve were hanging out in the Garden of Eden and God gave them only one rule to keep. He told them not to eat fruit from the tree of evil—"

"Actually, it was called 'the tree of the knowledge of good and evil' but close enough," interrupted Nick.

"Thanks. So a snake that's supposed to be possessed by Satan or something, talks Eve into eating the fruit from the tree, and she talks Adam into it and they both realize they're naked," I smiled again at the word, "and they try to hide from God. Is that close enough to the *real* story, Nick?"

"That's pretty good, Jared! You should teach a Bible study!"

"Don't push it!" I warned.

"As I said before," Nick continued, "Christianity is a relationship. And every relationship has to start somewhere in time. Christians believe that a long time ago, God created the first people and gave them a choice to trust him or not, just like we have the same kind of choice today.

VENTI JESUS PLEASE

"And that's basically the story of the first three chapters of the Bible. But here's what the story means. God created people because he wanted to relate to them. But a loving relationship can only exist if it includes the choice not to love. So God gave them a choice, and they chose to go against God. They turned their back on him and ruined the relationship they had with him. Adam and Eve's decision is the same decision to sin that each of us makes all the time."

"Wait. I want to make sure our terms are clear, just exactly what do *you* mean by that word 'sin'?" Jen asked. She was really getting into this.

Nick replied, "It means 'to miss the mark' or 'fall short of God's perfect standard.' It's anything that we do that misses the mark of God's perfection."

"So what happened to Adam and Eve when they chose to sin?" asked Jen.

I'll never forget Nick's blunt reply, because it fed into all my worst fears about a cruel and judgmental God. "They fell out of relationship with God and were condemned to die. You see, God made Adam and

Eve to live forever, but they chose to go their own way and that's how death entered the world. They didn't die right away physically, but their choice so damaged their relationship with God that they died spiritually. In other words, they became spiritually corrupted and self-centered. The rest of history shows the consequences of their choice to go their own way—sin all around us: war, famine, disease, broken families, crime, abuse."

"So you mean to tell me," I interrupted, "that all the crap in the world is a result of sin?"

"Yes."

"Okay, that's where I got you nailed, Nick!" I exclaimed, pounding the table.

"Hey, calm down, man. Remember, we're not debating, we're just having a friendly conversation about God, right?"

But I didn't miss a beat and plowed on, "Okay, a lot of wars throughout history were launched by Christians. Think of the Crusades in Medieval times.

VENTI JESUS PLEASE

Christians have been at the center of a lot of the wars in human history!"

Nick's head went down. Jesus-loving lotus position again, this time for thirty seconds or so.

"Cricket, cricket," Jen said, trying to break the silence with a little humor.

Finally looking up, Nick asked me, "So what you're saying is that if wars are the result of sin in the world and if Christians were responsible for some of these wars, then Christians are hypocrites?"

"Yes!" I knew I had him with this one. Game, set, match.

6

"I agree, Jared. Remember how this whole conversation got started—the newspaper story." Nick glanced over at where we'd left the newspaper. "I was telling you guys about how far I fall short, too. I'm a Christian and I struggle with sin like everyone else, including you. Since the beginning of time, we've all fallen short of what God's wanted us to be. I know that I fall way short. When a Christian sins, and all of us do, it doesn't negate the reality of God, it only shows how much we all need him in our lives."

VENTI JESUS PLEASE

I glanced at Jen and was surprised to see that she didn't look as skeptical as I was expecting her to.

"All I'm saying is this," Nick continued, "that as a Christian, I have an explanation for the problem of evil. The problem of evil is not God. It's us and our choices. He gave Adam and Eve free will in the Garden of Eden and they chose to disobey him. We've been choosing to disobey ever since. It's as simple as that."

"But wait a minute, Nick," Jen said. "Just what exactly is the problem of evil? Again, I'm playing catch up on all this God and sin stuff."

Jen wasn't stupid, she was just uninformed. I knew all too well that she had plenty of personal experience with the problem of evil because of all the bad scenes in her family triggered by her alcoholic dad. Maybe that was part of the dynamic that explained her level of interest in this surprisingly intense spiritual conversation.

Nick responded with a series of questions. "Have you ever wondered where evil came from?

How did it get into the world and into the human heart? Have you ever wanted to cheat on a test? Have you ever wondered why bad things happen to good people? Why there was something as horribly evil as the Holocaust? Or for that matter, why your dad can act like such a jerk sometimes?"

"Sure, we've all wondered that," Jen replied, looking at me to see if I agreed. I could tell by the uncomfortable look on her face that Nick's last question had hit close to home.

Nick continued, "The Bible's answer is that there are no good people." Reaching down for his backpack, he began to rummage through his stuff. Finally he pulled out his Bible, opened it up, and said, "Everything we've been talking about is in the Bible. It says right here in Romans 3:23, 'For all have sinned and fall short of the glory of God.' We have all lost the relationship with God that deep down we want and were created to have."

"Wait a minute, Nick," I interrupted, now getting a little angry. "I know some really bad people, but I also know some good people. My Aunt Sarah is the kindest person I've ever met. She gives money to the poor and volunteers at the Rescue Mission. You mean to tell me she's not a good person?"

Lotus position for Nick again…wait…wait…and then he was back again.

"Good compared to what?" Nick asked.

"What do you mean?" I asked back.

"I mean, I'm sure your Aunt Sarah does all those good things you say and is a good person when you compare her to other people you know. But that's not the kind of good that God is talking about. It's when any of us compare ourselves with God that we realize that nobody is truly good. Compared to a holy and perfect God, we all fall short," Nick continued. "We all miss the mark by a mile. Me, you, Jen and, yes, even your dear Aunt Sarah.

"God judges us, not just on the good deeds we do on the outside, but also on the reason we're doing those deeds. God sees right through our actions to our motives. What he sees is the selfishness that plagues us all—me included. We would all be in serious trouble if we relied on being a good person to get us to heaven because, at our core, we're all selfish. We're more concerned with ourselves than others."

"Well, I think I'm a good person," I stated boldly. "And I think Jen is, too."

"Alright, you're kind of forcing me into this, so here's the down and dirty. Are you ready?" Nick asked.

"I thought getting down and dirty was against your religion," Jen teased.

"You've heard of The 10 Commandments, right?" Nick asked, ignoring her jab.

Both Jen and I responded, "Duhhhhh!"

"Well, these commandments represent what God means when he talks about goodness and what he demands of us all the time, without exception, for all of our lives. Things like, don't put anyone or anything above God in importance in your life. I'm self-centered every day of my life, so check that one off. Or don't steal. That's not just talking about breaking and entering. It includes things like stealing time from your boss at work by calling your friends while you're on the clock, or stealing answers by cheating on homework or tests. And what about lying?"

Jen and I were quiet as Nick looked up and asked, "So how do you guys do when it comes to keeping The Big Ten?"

"Well, I've never murdered or anything like that," I said, trying to justify myself.

"Are you sure about that?" Nick was really pushing now. "Jesus said in Matthew 5 that if you hate your brother, you've murdered him in your heart. All of us have pictured strangling someone we're angry with. I know there have been a few times when I've felt like I could have strangled you, Jared."

We all laughed, but this was uncomfortable ground for me. My dad had been sending me the message for years that I didn't measure up, and now my best friend was telling me the same thing. Nice guy that I was, I was not good enough.

Nick continued, "Jesus also said in Matthew 5 that if you've lusted after a girl in your heart then, it's like you've had sex with her in your head, and therefore you've broken the spirit of these commandments. These are just a few of the Ten Commandments, and all of us have already blown it. No offense, but God's standard of pure goodness is something no one can live up to. It's why we need him in our lives."

No laughter this time.

"I'll tell you how I do," Nick went on. "I miss the mark continuously. I fell short of meeting God's perfect standard several times today."

"Murder someone, have you?" I asked with a slight smile.

"No, but the night is young," Nick shot back. "And since we got here, I've been jealous of your new Scion, I've been eyeing the hot barista way too many times, I ranted on about the preacher and dug through all my old baggage about my mom…need I go on?"

VENTI JESUS PLEASE

"She is hot, isn't she?" I said, looking over at the barista. I was totally with him on that point.

"So let me get this straight," Jen quickly pushed on, obviously uninterested in our hot barista banter. "You're saying that because Adam and Eve screwed up in the garden, all of us are, well, screwed?"

"I might have put it differently, but yes," Nick agreed. "When Adam and Eve sinned, they immediately covered themselves in fig leaves and hid themselves from God."

"Why?" Jen asked.

Nick responded, "Because they knew they had disobeyed what God had told them about not eating from the tree of the knowledge of good and evil. And for the first time they felt guilty and ashamed—that's why they hid themselves from God.

"And humanity has been playing hide and seek with God ever since. It's like we want to go our own way and do our thing, separate from God, but there's still something deep inside us that feels incomplete apart from him. Like I get this empty feeling whenever

I think about my father. I've told you before how I never knew my real dad. He and my mom were never married. Mom was kind of a partier and I was, well, one of the results of her lifestyle.

"So I have this empty spot inside of me, maybe because we're supposed to have a dad in our lives who cares about us," Nick continued. I glanced at Jen, a little concerned about how she was reacting to all this dad talk, since it was always a touchy subject with her. "Well, same thing with God. We're designed to have a relationship with God and when Adam and Eve messed up way back, they messed that up for all of us."

"I sorta know how you feel about the whole having a dad who's checked out routine," Jen said. "But I still don't get how what Adam and Eve did affects me."

"Well, the way my youth leader explained it was with a bottle of water and a drop of arsenic," Nick offered, grabbing his water bottle out of his backpack. "If you let this water bottle represent all of humanity and the poisonous arsenic represent the sin Adam and Eve introduced into the world, it's like they put a drop of arsenic in the water bottle. Would you take a drink of water that had only one drop of arsenic in it?"

"No," Jen responded.

"Why not?" Nick asked.

"Because it would poison me," she answered.

"And that's exactly what Adam and Eve's one sin did to the rest of humanity—it poisoned them spiritually. We come into the world poisoned by sin from the very beginning. Think about it. You don't have to teach little kids how to be bad—that comes naturally! You have to teach them how to obey and share and play nice—that doesn't come naturally! Make sense?"

Jen answered, "I guess so. But to say that we all fall short of God's perfect standard seems pretty harsh."

"Too harsh," I interjected. "I thought Christians believe that God is loving and forgiving. I'm not seein' the love here."

CHAPTER 6

"He is loving and forgiving," Nick said with a hint of frustration. "God is not like us, he is totally love, but he is also totally justice at the same time. He is so pure that he can't be around sin."

"Kind of like Superman and Kryptonite?" I inserted, half joking.

Jen probed further, asking, "And you're saying that no matter how many good things we do, we can never offset the bad ones we've already done?"

Nick took a swig of his bottled water before he answered simply, "Yes."

"So, I give up," I pushed back. "I mean the picture you're painting for us to accept or reject is pretty depressing. God made us. We screwed up. We're going to die, stand before some kind of divine judgment which, of course, we will fail, and probably end up going to hell and there's nothing we can do to change the situation. I mean, it all sounds empty and hopeless."

"And that's the difference between religion and the good news that Jesus talked about," Nick stated with what I sensed was relief that I'd travelled down the logic road and arrived at this depressing conclusion on my own.

At this point I wasn't feeling very good, and it wasn't because of the Frappe. I agreed that I'm not perfect, no one is. But it kinda seemed like God had set us up to fail.

"Okay, now I'm the confused one," Jen interrupted. "What do you mean?"

Nick explained, "Religion conveniently says that you can be good enough, that you can earn your way to heaven, that you can make it on your own. But the Bible says you can't make it on your own, that you're not good enough, that you *are* hopeless."

"I'm failing to get the 'good news' here," I mumbled. This was *not* making sense.

"Before you can fully appreciate the good news, you have to fully embrace the bad news. The antidote to the arsenic is only good news to those who know they've been poisoned. Just like the cure to cancer is only good news to you if you realize that you have cancer. This is where Jesus comes into the story. And Jesus is only good news to those who recognize that they have the cancer of sin in their souls and are looking for the cure. Does that make sense?" asked Nick.

"Not really. Not yet," Jen admitted. "Keep going and I'll tell you when I get it."

Nick continued, "Of all we've talked about up to now, the most important part is that the message of Christianity is the message of what Jesus said and did. And when he came, he told us that we all miss the mark. That we can never earn our way to heaven or into God's favor on our own. We miss the mark and are condemned, like Adam and Eve, to die. But God's remedy was to send his only Son, Jesus Christ, into the world to die in our place for our sin because he loved us so much."

"Yeah, yeah, yeah…" I interrupted, "we all know the story. Jesus suffered, died and rose from the dead three days later. It all just seems morbid to me."

VENTI JESUS PLEASE

"It's more morbid than you think," Nick agreed. "Jesus was beaten with a whip again and again and again—a whip that had pieces of nails and broken pottery tied into it. Soldiers beat him until he was ripped and bloody. After all this, they nailed him to a cross where he hung for six hours naked, bleeding and dying. It's much more morbid than most people imagine. You see those nice little crosses with an image of Jesus hanging gently on the cross and an expression of peace on his face. It was nothing like that. Jesus' death was incredibly brutal. But he went to it willingly."

"Okay, so I have a question for you," I shot back. "Why did God have to pick that way to forgive the sins of humanity? Why couldn't he have snapped his fingers and wiped out all the sins of everyone instead of crucifying his own Son? After all, he *is* supposed to be God?" After I asked this question, I could tell by Nick's deer-in-the-headlights expression that he was out of his league.

"Time for another bathroom break," Nick announced suddenly. He grabbed his backpack and bolted toward the restroom.

CHAPTER 6

"Something weird is going on with Nick," Jen said.

"Yeah, what's the deal? I wonder what's in that backpack," I mused. "And what do you think is up with all the meditative lotus position poses he's been pulling?"

"Why don't we try to find out?" Jen suggested with a conspiratorial smile.

I agreed. Anyway, the conversation had been getting so serious we needed something to lighten up the tone. Nick had been putting his pack on the floor right next to where he'd been sitting. Our plan was to use our feet under the table to slide the pack slowly toward one of us, next time he was in one of his meditative poses.

We were determined to get to the bottom of Nick's weirdness about his backpack.

7

"Alright, where were we?" Nick asked, throwing his backpack down on the chair next to him and unknowingly thwarting our plans.

Temporarily thrown off by this unexpected logistical shift, I kind of stumbled, "Uhh, uhh…we were talking about—"

Jen came to my rescue. "We were talking about why Jesus had to die such a horrible death on the cross to pay for the sins of humanity and why God couldn't have just snapped his fingers and forgiven everyone."

VENTI JESUS PLEASE

Nick looked at Jen and asked, "The way Jesus died really bothers you doesn't it, Jen?"

Jen shot back without hesitation, "Yeah, it does."

"Why?" Nick asked.

"Well, I hate violence and it's hard for me to imagine a God who would allow this level of violence on his own Son because everyone else screwed up," Jen admitted.

"Me too, Jen. It's hard for me to imagine that. But let me tell you about the very first verse in the Bible that I ever heard. It's John 3:16, and it goes like this: 'For God so loved the world that he gave his one and only Son, that whoever believes in him shall not perish but have eternal life.' God gave Jesus up to this violent, painful death because he loves us and wants to reestablish the relationship with us that was lost when Adam and Eve sinned. In that relationship, we can trust him, glorify him, find our purpose in life and live forever with him in heaven."

I could tell that Nick's words touched Jen deeply. And, to be honest, they kind of moved me too. For the first time, I thought to myself that if Christianity were really true, it would be the greatest love story ever. Imagine a God who would allow his son to sacrificially give his life in order to repair the broken relationship and be reunited with humanity. It was sort of like a heroic soldier falling on a grenade, knowingly giving his life to save others, but on some sort of grand, cosmic scale. Real people sometimes did amazing, self-sacrificing things like that, so even I was starting to catch a glimpse of how Jesus might be willing to do that for humanity.

But I still wasn't ready to buy what my friend was trying to sell.

"You never answered the question, Nick," I reminded him, breaking up the semi-solemn moment.

"What question?" Nick asked.

"Why did Jesus have to die? Why couldn't God just snap his fingers and forgive everyone?" I reminded him.

VENTI JESUS PLEASE

"Oh yeah," he said. "I did forget. But here it is. The reason Jesus had to die was because God is a God of justice. He set the world up so that there is cause and effect, and that means there are consequences for our bad choices and behaviors. In other words, he had to make things right. Since it is impossible for humans to make things right on their own, he had to make it right for them by sacrificing his own holy and perfect son in their place. Think of it in a courtroom setting. Jared, let's say you get a speeding ticket—"

Jen interrupted, "That's not hard to imagine. You think you're Super Mario in your new Scion!"

"No, I'm Jason Bourne!" I shot back.

Nick continued, "Better listen up, Jared, or I'll come at you like a Treadstone assassin!"

Jen got us back on track as we were about to go on a wild Matt Damon tangent by saying, "Okay, okay, sorry I got us sidetracked, so Jared gets a speeding ticket."

Nick leaned forward in his chair and continued, "Yeah, Jared actually gets caught speeding and gets a ticket, but say he can't afford to pay the fine. He is about to get sentenced to jail for his unpaid ticket but you, being the great girl that you are, pay his fine for him. He goes free because *you* paid *his* fine. That's what Jesus did. He paid our outstanding fine for us and we go free, if we put our faith and trust in him."

Jen added, "Except our 'ticket' is not for something simple like speeding, is it? It's for breaking God's law."

"Exactly!" Nick exclaimed, excited that Jen seemed to be getting it now that we were all once again fully engaged and Bourne-free. "And our sentence is not a fine or a few days in jail, but an eternity in hell, forever out of relationship with God. Because God is totally loving and totally just. And being loving *and* just, his solution was that Jesus would die in our place for our sin. Because Jesus, who was God, came to earth and entered into a human existence, he could die for other humans. Because he was God, his death on the cross fulfilled God's requirement for justice and was a supernaturally sufficient payment for our sin."

"I don't know, Nick. It's a good story, but it all sounds unbelievable and, to be honest, too good to be true. It really can't be that simple. We believe and we are forgiven for everything. It's got to be harder than that," Jen observed, but her voice quavered and she sounded like she was hoping Nick could convince her it was all true.

Nick responded, "My youth leader said last week in his talk that faith is trusting in a person I've never met, to take me to a place I've never been. How easy is it to trust in Jesus, a person we've never met, to forgive us for all of our sins and take us to heaven, a place we've never been?" Nick answered his own rhetorical question, "It's so easy that a child could do it and a 'religious' person could choke on it."

"I don't know, Nick," Jen objected again. "You're saying that Jesus is the way to a meaningful life and to heaven and that's fine. But what about Buddha or Mohammed or whoever? I really don't know anything about those other religions. But it seems to me that even if Jesus is cool, so are all those other religions, right?"

"No," Nick responded while reaching for his backpack. He unzipped it and reached in to find his Bible. Opening it up, he flipped through several pages until he finally found what he was looking for, and continued on saying, "Jesus said in John 14:6, 'I am *the* way and *the* truth and *the* life. No one comes to the Father except through me.'" Then looking up at me, he said something that got my blood boiling, "Jesus claimed a relationship with him was the *only* way to heaven."

"You mean to tell me that all other religions are on the 'highway to hell'?" I asked angrily.

"No. Not all *other* religions—*all* religions are bound for hell. The word 'religion' comes from the Latin word that means 'to bind back.' *All* religions are trying in one way or another to bind themselves back to God through good deeds, sacrifices, baptism, codes, creeds or whatever. All of it falls short.

"True Christianity, I'm talking here about the relationship with God—not the religion—is not about the ways people try to earn their way back to God at all," Nick explained. "It's about recognizing that there is no way to 'bind ourselves back' to God through our good deeds, because compared to God's perfection, our good deeds are like filthy rags.

"True Christianity," he went on, "is realizing that God bound himself to humanity through his Son Jesus Christ, and that Jesus allowed himself to be bound to a cross for our sins. He was bound up in a tomb and set free from the bonds of death after three days when he rose from the dead. And Jesus offers to unbind us forever from the penalty of sin, if we simply trust in him alone as our only hope for forgiveness!"

Nick was on a roll so he kept going, flipping through the pages of his Bible again. "Jesus said in John 6:47, 'I tell you the truth, he who believes has everlasting life.' You see, at the end of the day, the gift of forgiveness, of everlasting eternal life, of heaven, of a personal, permanent relationship with God, is not achieved by our good deeds, but received through faith. It's not a matter of trying, but trusting. And once I put my faith and trust in him alone for the free gift of my forgiveness, God himself became my heavenly Father forever. He will love me always. He will always be there for me. No matter what I've done in the past or how I fall short now—and I often do—or how I'll mess up in the future, he will love me unconditionally. He will hear all of my prayers and hold me tightly through the storms of life."

Silence.

8

But I couldn't keep silent for long. I was steaming as I shouted, "That's BS!" A few customers looked my way in disgust, but I was too outraged to be distracted for long. "How can a God who is supposed to be so loving send people of different religions who happen to reject Jesus to hell? How is that fair?"

"Calm down, man," Nick said. Then he grabbed my empty Venti cup and continued, "Okay, a few weeks back in youth group, I was part of this skit that kind of illustrates this. If you promise not to cuss at me, I'll share it with you," Nick said with a half smile.

VENTI JESUS PLEASE

I threw Jen a weak smile, knowing she didn't like conflict, and then turned back to Nick. "Sorry, dude. It's just hard for me to hear this stuff. It seems narrow-minded to think Jesus is the only way to heaven."

To my surprise, Nick agreed. "It does seem narrow-minded. But being open-minded means we must entertain the logical possibility that the only way to heaven could be through Jesus and Jesus alone. If we don't consider the possibility that Jesus could be the only way, we're not really open-minded. Right?"

Jen reminded me that Nick had been part of Brentwood's championship debate team for the last two years and encouraged me just to nod my head yes. "Okay," I admitted, "being the open-minded and strikingly handsome atheist that I am, I'm willing to consider the possibility that Jesus could be the only way to heaven—but I want to go on record right now and make it clear that I don't like the idea one bit."

"Okay, I get that, but give me a minute, I need to find what I want to show you…I know it's in here somewhere," Nick muttered, looking through his pack. Finally, he pulled out three wrinkled pieces of paper and laid them on the table. Then holding up my empty Venti cup again, he said, "Okay, we're in Starbucks, right?"

"Duhhh," I responded.

"This skit we did for youth group last week was called *Spiritual Starbucks*. Would you mind if I read it to you?" Nick asked.

"Only if you promise to do all the voices yourself," Jen teased.

Straightening the crumpled papers out as much as he could, he sat up and shifted into his drama mode. Nick was on the debate team, but he'd also been in the drama club in past years. He made me laugh. He cleared his throat and began to read the script, offering a different voice as he read each character's lines.

BARISTA: Welcome to Spiritual Starbucks, may I take your order?

VENTI JESUS PLEASE

CUSTOMER 1: Yes, I'd like a triple *Buddha, Mocha Mohammed Latte*, with an extra shot of religion.

BARISTA: Sure, would you like a *Pious Pastry* with that?

CUSTOMER 1: No, I'm good.

BARISTA: How about a *Hari Krishna Cookie*?

CUSTOMER 1: No, I just ate. Just the drink.

BARISTA: Great, that will be your eternal destiny.

CUSTOMER 1: Is that all?

BARISTA: Yeah, we're running a special. And you get your destiny extra hot...hot as hell, actually.

CUSTOMER 1: Awesome. *(Moves over to wait for his drink. CUSTOMER 2 approaches.)*

BARISTA: Welcome to Spiritual Starbucks. How may I help you?

CHAPTER 8

CUSTOMER 2: Yes, um, this is my first time here…so I don't quite know what to order?

BARISTA: Well, we're glad to have you, sir. Would you like a cold drink, like a *Frappuccino*, or something hot, like a latte?

CUSTOMER 2: I guess something cold.

BARRISTA: Great, a *Frappuccino*. What kind of *Frappe* would you like?

CUSTOMER 2: What kind do you have? *(People in line are getting frustrated.)*

BARISTA: Well, we have your *Mohammed Mocha, Wildberry Wiccan*—

BARISTA 2: *(Cutting in.)* *Caramel Cult Frappuccino, Quasi Jesus Frappe*—

CUSTOMER 2: Why only a *Quasi Jesus*?

BARISTA: Nobody wants him full strength anymore, sir.

VENTI JESUS PLEASE

CUSTOMER 2: Umm, well, how about a *Mormon Frappuccino*? I've heard those are good.

BARISTA: Yeah, sure we have that—

BARISTA 2: But it only comes in decaf.

CUSTOMER 2: Okay, do you have chai tea?

BARISTA: Yes, *Tai Chi Chai Tea*.

CUSTOMER 2: Umm… Okay, I'll have a *Quasi Wildberry Wiccan*, with a shot of *Caramel Cult*.

BARISTA: What size?

CUSTOMER 2: What do you mean?

BARISTA: Well, we have Tall, Grande and Venti.

CUSTOMER 2: What does that mean?

BARISTA: We have small, medium and large. Tall, if you only want a little bit of religion in your life, enough to make you spiritual, but not enough to drive you crazy. Grande, if you want to make a full on commitment to the belief system.

CUSTOMER 2: What does that mean?

BARISTA: Well, if you want to go to the church, the mosque, the coven or whatever meeting every week.

CUSTOMER 2: And what about Venti?

BARISTA: Venti is if you want to be a full-on fanatic for your particular religion.

CUSTOMER 2: Since I'm new to this and I may want to change drinks later on, I'll just go for a Tall this time.

BARISTA: Is that all?

CUSTOMER 2: Yes.

BARISTA: No *Pious Pastries* or *Krishna Cookies*?

VENTI JESUS PLEASE

CUSTOMER 2: Umm... *(Crowd behind him groans loudly.)* No.

BARISTA: Okay. Let's just ring this up here... That will be your soul.

CUSTOMER 2: Great! Didn't have a need for it anyway. *(Moves over to receive his drink. CUSTOMER 3 approaches.)*

BARISTA; Welcome to Spiritual Starbucks, sir. May I take your order?

CUSTOMER 3: Yes, I'd like a Venti *Full Strength Jesus*, please.

BARISTA: Sorry, sir, but we don't serve *Full Strength Jesus* here. You can have a *Quasi Jesus*, with a shot of something else to spice it up.

CUSTOMER 3: No. I just want straight Jesus please… extra hot. *(More groans from the line.)*

BARISTA 2: Sir. *(Whispering.)* Do you know why we don't serve Venti *Full Strength Jesus* here?

CUSTOMER 3: No.

BARISTA: Because quite honestly, it's a mess. Once we served *Full Strength Jesus*, those who ordered it never wanted anything else. Ever. As a matter of fact, once they ordered it, they never were thirsty for anything again. Which means they didn't order again. Which means it hurt business. As a matter of fact, they started pestering the other customers and trying to get them to go with the Venti *Full Strength Jesus*. Those who like *Full Strength Jesus* think it is the way, the truth, the life and the drink that will quench their thirst for all time.

CUSTOMER 3: Well, that's how I want him. Straight and full strength.

BARISTA: Well, you came to the wrong place… NEXT!!!

Nick looked up and added, "Fade to black." He took a seated bow while Jen and I mock clapped. I had to admit it was kinda lame and kinda funny at the same time. But it made a strong point. Still, I had some questions.

VENTI JESUS PLEASE

"Okay, okay. That was kinda lame," I said, "But how do you know that 'Venti Jesus with nothing added' is the only way to heaven? You say that Jesus was God and man. Why couldn't he just have been a man? A good guy? A spiritual teacher? Don't get me wrong, I believe that Jesus existed and did some good things, but where do you get off claiming that he was God?"

Nick went into his meditative state again while Jen jumped in, "Hey, Jared, that's a good question, but before we get in much deeper, how much time do we still have before we need to be back at the school for the play?"

I told Jen that we still had twenty minutes before we needed to head out.

9

Looking back up, Nick reengaged once again and said, "There are only a few options for who Jesus really could be."

"What do you mean?" I asked.

"C. S. Lewis, the guy who wrote all the Narnia stories, was also a Christian philosopher. He said that there were really only three options for Jesus. He is either Lord, a lunatic or a liar."

Jen countered, "That seems a little extreme. Why couldn't he just be, like Jared said, a spiritual leader and teacher?"

VENTI JESUS PLEASE

"Because Jesus claimed to be God again and again throughout the gospels."

Jen and I must have both looked confused because Nick jumped back in to explain. "The gospels are the first four books of the New Testament that tell the story of the birth, life, ministry, death and resurrection of Jesus from four different perspectives." Then he flipped his Bible open to read us a part where Jesus claimed to be God. "'I give them eternal life, and they shall never perish; no one can snatch them out of my hand. My Father, who has given them to me, is greater than all; no one can snatch them out of my Father's hand. I and the Father are one.' Again the Jews picked up stones to stone him, but Jesus said to them, 'I have shown you many great miracles from the Father. For which of these do you stone me?' 'We are not stoning you for any of these,' replied the Jews, 'but for blasphemy, because you, a mere man, claim to be God.'" Looking up, Nick added, "That was from John 10, verses 28 through 33."

"I see what you mean," I admitted. "Those are some pretty hard statements to argue against. If the words written there are accurate, then it does look like Jesus claimed to be God himself."

Jen interrupted, "Dumb blonde moment here. I still don't get how his claiming to be God gives us only three options for who he could be: Lord, lunatic or liar."

I answered before Nick could. "Because if he claimed to be God and wasn't, then there are only two possibilities—he was a deluded, crazy, whacked-out nut job or he was lying to everybody."

Nick was impressed. "Hey, that's pretty good, Jared. You should've been on the debate team."

"Yeah, well, I didn't want to hang out with all the nerds," I said, jabbing back at him.

Nick stuck his tongue out at me. But before he could land one back at me, Jen redirected us back to the serious stuff by asking, "Okay Nick, that all makes sense. But doesn't that scare you some? I mean if Jesus wasn't God, then he was either insane or evil."

VENTI JESUS PLEASE

Another extended, awkward moment hung between us as Nick stared at his lap. This one took even longer than the previous silent interludes we'd almost grown used to.

Finally, looking up, Nick answered, "If Jesus was insane, then how could he speak such a radical message about God's love that would change the course of human history? How could he have shared so many powerful messages of truth that would improve society, relationships and bring hope? How could a nut job have such a huge impact on the history of the world—on every level?

"And if he was a liar, don't you think his disciples would have caught on after three years of being with him day and night? Don't you think the religious leaders who hated him would have found out and used those lies against him?"

"I dunno, maybe. But how do you know, how do you really know that he was God?" Jen asked.

"Because he rose from the dead—and when he rose from the dead, he proved that he was who he claimed to be."

Me, believe someone could rise from the dead? I'd just as soon believe in a literal six day creation. So I countered, "Well, how do you know that he actually rose from the dead? Maybe he wasn't really killed and they just thought he was dead."

Nick looked down again for another awkwardly uncomfortable length of time before he jumped back in and said, "Well, a couple weeks ago at the Easter service, my pastor talked about exactly that issue. First off, he said that it's important to know that the Romans were experts at killing. Around the same time that Jesus was killed, they crucified something like 6,000 people in one day. They knew what it took to kill somebody. They knew when somebody was dead. They made sure that Jesus was dead when he was hanging on the cross by sticking a spear into his rib cage and watching the blood and water flow out, confirming that they'd ruptured the fluid sack that surrounded his heart."

"Ok, fine, so Jesus was dead. What's your point?" I pushed.

Nick continued, "He was dead and buried, not the typical kind of burial we're familiar with. He was mummified and entombed in a cave and 'locked in' by a huge stone that was rolled over the entrance. Well-trained Roman soldiers were dispatched to guard the tomb to make sure nobody tried to steal the body and claim 'He is risen!' Three days later, the Bible says, he rose physically from the grave. The soldiers passed out, they were so afraid of what was going on. Then over the next forty days, Jesus appeared to over 500 witnesses. These witnesses claimed to have seen him first-hand."

"So what?" I challenged, "They could have just been saying that they saw the resurrected Jesus. They could have been making it up!"

"Yes, they could have. But when you think about it, that's not actually very likely," Nick replied. "Because many of these witnesses were tortured and murdered for their claim that they had seen the risen Jesus. Now, as someone has said, some people will die for what they think to be the truth, but nobody will die for what they know to be a lie."

"I don't mean to hurt your feelings, Nick," Jen shared, "but I think this all sounds far-fetched."

"Me too," I agreed.

"Well, then both of you have a gigantic task in front of you," Nick declared.

"What?" we both asked in unison.

"You have to find a better explanation for how we got here, what life is all about, why there's evil in the world, what redemption looks like and means, why we feel guilty about some things and what happens after we die. The story of Christianity answers all these questions and more. So what's your explanation for all of it?"

10

I jumped in headfirst and stated flatly, "I've already told you mine. I don't believe in God."

"That's not telling me your explanation. That's just telling me what you *don't* believe. What do you believe?" Nick challenged again.

I laid it out straight up. "I believe we're the result of evolution. That we live, that we die and that's basically it."

Nick pushed back. "So then why do you feel guilty when you do something wrong?"

VENTI JESUS PLEASE

"I don't see how that has anything to do with—" I stopped myself mid-sentence, paused for a moment and thought out loud, "I guess I've always assumed that our ideas of right and wrong come from our parents. And that it all has something to do with what's in the common good for the survival of the species.

"But the problem with that theory is that what's in the best interests of the survival of the species is often entirely opposite from what's in the best interests of your own personal survival. So for example, why would a soldier ever fall on a grenade to save his buddies? How would those directly contradictory survival instincts ever get programmed into us?"

"I don't really know," I conceded.

"So maybe," Nick continued, "God created us in his image, with a conscience. Maybe he gave us this conscience to help us determine what's noble from what's shameful—what's right from what's wrong. Maybe he created us with the capacity to feel noble or guilty feelings as an inner reminder that he's there, he's watching and that someday we will give an account to him for everything we've ever done wrong."

It was a "holy crap" moment for me. If Nick was right, then I was in trouble. I think he sensed my discomfort, because he turned his gaze off of me and looked over at Jen and asked, "And what's your explanation for all this, Jen?"

"Ummmm…" was all Jen said. She seemed a little blind-sided by this turn in the conversation, too. Nick stayed silent, and had an odd expression on his face, like he thought watching us squirm under his questioning was good for us somehow. Eventually Jen broke the silence and said hesitantly, "I guess I don't know. But I figure I'll just find out when I die."

At which point I jumped back in. "But if what Nick is saying is true, then when you die it will be too late. You'll be burning in the flames of hell, getting poked and prodded by the devil's pitchfork. Right, Nick?"

"Something like that," Nick agreed. I could tell he wasn't quite sure whether to smile at what I had intended to be a joke.

VENTI JESUS PLEASE

"Oh, no," I blurted suddenly. "Never mind the hell thing, I've got my own private hell waiting in the wings for me, 'cause I just remembered I forgot to tell my mom I wouldn't be around for dinner tonight. That's all I need, another lecture from dad about responsibility and communication and blah, blah, blah." Grabbing my phone, I quickly realized it was out of juice. My mom had no doubt been trying to call me. There were probably ten messages asking me where I was.

"Hey, Nick, can I borrow your phone?" I asked.

"Uh, I guess," he answered, bringing it up from under the table. An uncomfortable look flashed across his face as he hesitantly handed it to me saying, "I'm watching for an important text, so make it quick, okay?"

Just as I was about to dial home, a text came up. "Oh, here it is. Is it a girl that's so important? Let me check it for you," I said, while opening it.

"NO!!!" Nick said way too loudly to be cool. He stood up to grab for the phone.

CHAPTER 10

Nick was hiding something, and as I looked down at the text it became obvious that it wasn't a girl. The text message simply read: *Ask thm wht hppns 2 a soul aftr deth n thr wrld view*.

I started laughing like a crazy man.

"What?" Jen asked, wanting to know what was up. Nick fell back in his chair, looking like a three year old caught with his hand in the cookie jar.

"Our little Christian friend here has been cheating," I said laughing. But underneath the laugh, I was a little steamed. Then with a sudden burst of insight I exclaimed, "And we were thinking that every time your head went down you were praying or meditating or something. Here we thought that you were probably the smartest person on the planet by knowing all this stuff and instead you're getting fed answers by—who's texting you, man?" I asked.

"My youth leader," Nick said with all the blood drained from his already pale face. He continued his confession while Jen and I laughed some more. "When I first went into the restroom I called him and asked him what I should do and he suggested that I text him quick questions and he would text me back quick answers and some questions to ask you guys. He's really smart about all this stuff and I knew he'd know what to say when I didn't. He talks about this stuff all the time in youth group."

Jen was still smiling when she asked, "So you didn't really have to go to the restroom? You were just getting argument ammo from your youth leader?"

"No. I really had to go. But while I was in there I called him, both times."

"Ewww. Once again, thanks for the graphic description," Jen said, scrunching up her nose in disgust.

"I'm really sorry, guys," Nick went on. "It's just that this is such an important conversation, I desperately wanted to get it right—you know, say the right things, have the right answers. In debate tournaments, we get pretty good at sounding like experts, even when we don't *really* know what we're talking about. But this discussion wasn't about winning a debate. I really wanted to give you solid, insightful answers to your questions." Caring, considerate Nick's genuine concern for us was coming through loud and clear. "And," he added with an embarrassed grin, "I might as well admit it, part of me also just plain didn't want to look stupid in front of my friends. I guess you could say that's one of my weak spots."

While we'd been talking, I'd scrolled through the text chain of questions and answers on Nick's phone. His youth leader had definitely been feeding him answers, but not all the answers. Nick knew enough on his own to stand his ground. Or at least I thought he did.

"Okay, since you explained everything else, why not tell us what's in your backpack that you don't want us to know about? You've been pretty possessive of it this afternoon," I said.

Nick reached in and grabbed two books. One was titled *More Than a Carpenter* and the other was called *A Case for Christ*. I'd never heard of either. He threw the books on the table with an embarrassed look.

Jen grabbed one and I grabbed the other and we started flipping through them. They were well-worn, underlined and had notes written in the margins. While we looked through them Nick explained that both these authors, Josh Mcsomething and Lee Storebell, or whatever, were both one-time skeptics of Christianity who had taken on the challenge of examining the evidence for Jesus being the Son of God. After extensive research, both had become convinced Jesus was who he said he was.

"Were you looking stuff up in the bathroom, too?" Jen asked.

"Yes," Nick admitted.

"Gross!" she said, throwing her book back down on the table. "Pass me the Purell hand sanitizer goop."

"Why are they so marked up?" I asked.

Nick's answer surprised me. "I've been studying them for months trying to get ready for this conversation," he said simply.

"What do you mean?" Jen asked.

CHAPTER 10

"I've been praying for the last year for a conversation like this to happen with you and Jared...and Kailey. I know that after we graduate, we'll all be going our separate ways and I wanted to tell you guys about Jesus before it was too late."

"I know you've tried to bring it up with me a bunch of different times, and I shut you down every time," I admitted.

I couldn't help but be a little touched by Nick's sincerity. Jen expressed my sentiments when she asked, "So you've been studying all these facts and stuff because you really care about us and you don't want to see us go to hell?"

"Right," Nick said, girding himself for a follow-up zinger.

11

But no zinger came. To be honest, this whole conversation hadn't been as bad as I'd thought it would be. In fact, now that I thought about it, Nick was just laying it out there for us. We had a real friend who truly believed that if we didn't trust in Jesus or whatever, we'd end up in hell. The fact that he had been praying a whole year for an opportunity and studying for this conversation like it was some final exam impressed me. I'm not kidding. It really did.

"I'm sorry I deceived you guys with the texting. Will you forgive me?" Nick asked. I was a little surprised by how serious his apology sounded. "I should have just been straight up with you that I wasn't quite ready yet for all your questions. I should have just said 'I don't know,' instead of sneaking text message answers from my youth leader."

"Of course we forgive you, Nick," Jen said for the both of us. "Personally, I think it's kind of sweet that you care so much about us that you were willing to do anything to get us the right answers."

Nick continued, "Well, speaking of the 'right answers,' I've got something else to admit to you."

"What's it this time," I joked. "Did you sneak Jesus pills into our Frappes when we weren't looking?"

He smiled and said, "No, no. It's just that I've not told you the real reason I became a Christian, and it wasn't because of any of the facts I just shared with you. As a matter of fact, I hadn't even heard any of this stuff before I became a Christian. It was years later before I discovered all this amazing evidence for the Christian faith."

CHAPTER 11

"So what got you to believe Christianity was true?" Jen asked, genuinely curious.

I was actually a little intrigued myself. I knew Nick didn't come from a religious background. His mom was definitely not the church-going type.

"Well, like you already know, I've never met my real father. But I don't think I've ever given you the full picture of how bad things were for me when I was a kid. You see, Mom's been married three times, but none of her marriages have lasted longer than a couple years. All the guys she married were jerks. One guy named Paul used to beat me up when he got drunk. I remember as a kid, wondering what life was all about. I even thought about suicide. I mean, I was ten years old and already thinking about blowing my brains out. Can you believe that?"

"No," I stated flatly, shocked at what I was hearing.

Nick continued with an emotional edge in his voice. "In fifth grade, this kid, Jeremy, transferred to my elementary school mid-year. He and I became friends right off. There was something about him I really liked."

In my mind, I knew exactly what Nick was talking about. It sounded much like the way I'd so naturally connected with him back when we were freshmen. Nick went on with his story. "One day we were skateboarding and he just started talking to me about God. To be honest, I had never thought much about God or anything like that. But it caught my attention.

"I ended up going to church with him and his family on Easter. The preacher was talking about God in a way that really grabbed me. He talked about God as a father in heaven who longs to have a relationship with us, who loved us so much that he sent his own son to earth to be sacrificed for our sins—so that we could be in relationship with him. I remember getting a strange feeling in my gut when the preacher shared that Jesus rose from the dead and how that was the real meaning of Easter. I thought that if this story was true it was the greatest thing in the world."

"Why did you think it was so great?" Jen asked softly.

"Because I knew if it was true, somebody really loved me. Someone loved me enough to die for me." Nick's voice quavered as he answered.

Uncomfortable, I jumped in and asked bluntly, "So what'd ya do?"

Nick looked me square in the eyes and said, "Right there in church, I asked God to be my dad, and I put my trust in Jesus to save me from my sins and to give me hope."

Nick paused for a moment, but when both Jen and I stayed quiet, he continued, "On the way home, I told Jeremy's family what I'd done and his mom gave me a Gospel of John to read. I read the whole thing from cover to cover that night before I went to bed."

"I'll bet it felt amazing to finally find a dad who really loved you," Jen added, her eyes slowly starting to well up.

VENTI JESUS PLEASE

Nick continued, "Yeah. I didn't know any of the facts about who created the world, or whether it evolved, or any of the evidences for Jesus rising from the dead or whatever. All I knew was that I was a sinner, that I deserved hell, that Jesus died for me and that God loved me. That night I literally cried myself to sleep, knowing for the first time, that I had a dad who loved me unconditionally. I had a dad who would never beat me, would never leave me, would never condemn me. I had a dad, a heavenly Father, who loved me so much that he sacrificed his own Son so that I could become his adopted son. That's why I became a Christian, guys."

While Nick had been talking, my uneasiness had been building. And now, suddenly, in the silence that had descended, I was thinking thoughts and feeling feelings I'd never had before. I was seriously wondering if there was a God—and if he could love someone like me. This was most unsettling.

But Nick wasn't done, and to be honest, I was glad, because at that point, I was afraid of talking for fear of going into emotional overload. "Jen, you've mentioned in the past that you see something in me that's different from other guys. What you see is not me—it's Jesus *in* me. He's my hope, my joy and he alone satisfies the deep longings of my soul like nothing else can.

"You guys are always asking me why I don't go partying with you on the weekends. It's not because I'm above it. I'm not. I guess you could say I've ordered a Venti *Full Strength Jesus*, and because Jesus is on the inside of my soul, the only thing that makes me truly happy is pleasing him."

"Dude, you always seem to be happy, like, you're never out there trying to escape from the day-to-day grind like the rest of us. I mean, that's what the partying is really all about—escape time," I added.

"Don't get me wrong, Jared. I've got problems like everyone else. You know how devastated I was when Brittany dumped me last year. Did it hurt? Yes. What got me through? Jesus. What's getting me through now that I won't be getting an athletic scholarship 'cause I messed up my knee and had to drop track? Jesus. What's going to get me through as I work my way through college? Jesus. What will get me through whatever comes my way down the road? Jesus.

VENTI JESUS PLEASE

"It may seem like Jesus is just a crutch for me to lean on. He's not. This may sound weird, but he's not my crutch, he's my stretcher. He's my everything. He makes my life worth living. It's not the facts of creation verses evolution, not the Lord, lunatic, liar stuff that gives me hope—it's Jesus himself. All those facts and stuff give me mental confidence that my Christian faith is on firm footing, but it's Jesus who meets the deepest needs of my soul. It was Jesus who convinced me he was real—not human arguments. He came into my life and changed everything."

12

When I glanced over at Jen, her eyes were misty. As soon as she saw me looking at her, the tears started to slip out.

Deep down, I knew why. She'd spilled her guts often enough about the battles that raged at home between her alcoholic dad and her religious rules mom. I knew she was emotionally out there on her own, distant from both her parents.

"For years I've been looking for ways to escape all the crap at home," Jen said, tears pouring down her cheeks now. "Escaping the pain—that's really what all the partying and sex are about. But that stuff hasn't changed anything…in fact, in some ways it's just made things worse. I always walk away feeling used and empty, and feeling like, what's the point. And guilty, sometimes I just feel like everything wrong in my life is so my fault—" She buried her face in her hands and just sat there sobbing.

Nick shifted over to the empty chair next to her and put a reassuring hand on top of hers. I leaned over and put my arm around her shoulders.

"I, I—" she struggled to get control and push the words out.

Amidst the tears, she explained haltingly, "I need—something. I so want a—a—a dad who will love me. I so want to—to be for—forgiven."

And now for the most awkward moment of my entire life, right there in our favorite Starbucks in front of complete strangers, Jen told Nick that she wanted to become a Christian. I guess you could say she was, according to the little skit, ordering a Venti *Full Strength Jesus* for the first time.

It was weird and moving at the same time. It was so weird, I glanced around the place, wondering if everyone was staring at us. But they were all absorbed in their own little worlds.

Jen was crying. Nick was crying. And once again, I was feeling a little emotional myself. It wasn't because I wanted to become a Christian right then and there like Jen. It was because for the first time, I viewed Christianity as something different than some rule-riddled religion. I saw it as a beautiful story that, if true, was the greatest thing in the history of humanity. No wonder Jen was opting in. Who wouldn't want to believe it could all be that simple, if they could simply suspend their rational thought process and take the leap of faith?

Nick's voice pulled me back to the present. "... saying a particular prayer to God won't launch you into a relationship with Jesus," he told Jen. "Only trusting in Jesus to forgive your sins will open the door to a real and intimate relationship with God. Saying a prayer to God is just a way to let God know that today you've chosen to become his child. Make sense?"

VENTI JESUS PLEASE

Jen just nodded.

"Can I lead you through a prayer to God?" Nick asked.

"Yes," she said, still sniffling.

"Now saying a prayer doesn't make you a Christian. It's just a way to let God know that you are accepting the free gift of his love," Nick repeated again for emphasis.

Jen nodded.

"Repeat these words after me," Nick said softly, as he and Jen both closed their eyes. "Dear God—"

"Dear God—" she repeated.

"I know I've messed up."

Starting to cry again, she whispered, "I know I've messed up."

"I know that I could never be good enough to earn my way into your perfect heaven."

CHAPTER 12

She wiped her cheek with the back of her hand and said, "I know that I could never be good enough to earn my way into your perfect heaven."

"But right now, I believe that Jesus died for all my sins."

She repeated these words with more confidence. I could tell she was really sincerely talking to God.

Nick continued, "And I trust him alone as my only hope of forgiveness, right now."

She repeated, sniffling again.

Nick was choked up too, and his voice was still quavering as he wrapped it up, "Thank you for being my heavenly Father and making me your child."

Jen lost it again, but eventually was able to get the words out.

Nick closed out the prayer by saying, "Jesus, I'm so excited about my new relationship with you that's starting here and now and that will last forever."

VENTI JESUS PLEASE

When they both opened their eyes and looked up, they hugged each other and before I could stop myself, I joined in. Here we were in a group hug in the middle of Starbucks, their tears still flowing and my mind still racing.

As we got up to leave, Nick invited both of us to come to his next youth group meeting, since they were going to be talking about the reliability of the Bible. Youth group didn't sound quite as Amish to me this time.

Then Nick dug into his backpack one more time and pulled out two small, identical, paperback books. Gospels of John, he called them. He explained that John was the one book of the Bible that was written to people who didn't believe in Jesus. He asked us both if we would read it later that night, after we had all watched *Grease* together. We both said yes.

So much for the after-party...I told you my plans were going to be ruined.

Actually though, I'm a little curious. I can party anytime—and usually do—but there's something intriguing about this God stuff. Maybe there's something to it.

Maybe.

If you can't tell, I'm not yet convinced. But I'm definitely in a different place than I was an hour ago.

Nick told us he wasn't going to push us to buy into it. He didn't. He painted a picture, though. His perspective was interesting to hear and discuss. I don't know for sure if I buy all his facts—or his text messaging youth leader's facts, for that matter. But it's the message of Jesus himself that's got me thinking on a whole different level.

I wonder what Sandra D is going to think about all this. Speaking of Kailey—we gotta go.

All for one, and one for all.

▶ If you'd like to read the Gospel of John, go to www.dare2share.org/ventijesus.

▶ If you want to read more about the facts that support Christianity, check out *More Than a Carpenter* by Josh McDowell or *A Case for Christ* and *A Case for a Creator* by Lee Strobel.

▶ If you'd like to order more *Venti Jesus Please* books to pass along to your friends, go to www.dare2share.org/ventijesus.

▶ If you enjoyed this book, follow Jared and his friends in the sequel to *Venti Jesus Please*. Pick up a copy of *Firestarter* at dare2share.org and see what can happen when just one Christian is passionate about sharing the message of Jesus on their high school campus.

Greg Stier is the President of Dare 2 Share and has equipped teenagers across the United States to share Jesus with their friends with courage, clarity and compassion. He, his wife Debbie, and their two children, Jeremy and Kailey, live in Arvada, Colorado. For more information, check out his blog at www.gregstier.org.